```
D1633361
```

We constantly travel the globe to discover new gemstones.
Scan this QR code on a mobile device to read the latest news.

The Little Book of Gemstones Csarite
www.tggc.com

All enquiries should be directed to:
The Genuine Gemstone Company Limited, Unit 2D
Eagle Road, Moons Moat
Redditch, Worcestershire, B98 9HF

ISBN: 978-0-9559972-7-3
Published by The Genuine Gemstone Company Limited
Designed by The Genuine Gemstone Company Limited

THE LITTLE BOOK OF GEMSTONES

Csarite

TURKISH MIRACLE

By Steve Bennett

INTRODUCTION

Welcome to the world of Mother Nature's treasures: a world full of colourful locations, colourful people, colourful stories and, of course - colourful gems.

This series has been written in an A to Z encyclopaedic format, so that you can dip in and out at your leisure. Whenever you come across a new gemstone or hear someone mention a jewellery term that you have not heard before, you can easily use these books to quickly find out more.

Steve Bennett

Csarite

TURKISH MIRACLE

Mining for Csarite
with Steve and Rod

In August 2011, TGGC's Rod Jinks and Steve Bennett headed to Turkey to find out more about one of the rarest and most sought after gemstones on the planet - Csarite. They even got to mine some!

It's unusual to be taking a gem hunting trip within Europe: well, in fact where I am off to is not strictly within Europe, as Turkey still remains just outside of the union. Although there are many feldspar mines in the country, none of them are reportedly uncovering any commercial grade gemstones, and to date the only gemstone uncovered in this large, mainly mountainous country is the now world famous Diaspore.

My regular cameraman Matt (my eldest son), couldn't come on this adventure and therefore I threw the invite open to the presenters asking for one of them to join me. Without question they all wanted to visit this incredible gem's birthplace, but when I mentioned it to my buddy Rod Jinks, his grin and sheer excitement couldn't be ignored, so I decide Rod would come along and operate the cameras.

We flew into the picturesque town of Bodrum on the southern coast of Turkey. After arriving late in the evening we decided to turn in early, so as to be ready for the day ahead; a day that I had been waiting for ever since 2006 when The Genuine Gemstone Company became the world's exclusive supplier of Diaspore. Since that time Diaspore has risen to be one of the greatest gem stories of the last 20 years. Today, leading designers all around the world

The beauty of the surrounding area is breathtaking - just like Csarite itself.

are creating one-of-a-kind masterpieces with the gem. From Erica Courtney in the USA to Daniel Gibbing, from Sarah Bennett to Stephen Webster in the UK, all have been captivated by the gem's array of magical optical properties. Stephen Webster at the Las Vegas show in 2011 unveiled a necklace featuring the largest Diaspore unearthed so far: weighing in at 96 carats, the gem was set in 18k gold and was on sale at £1.5 million dollars (approximately £1 million pounds).

The next morning Murat, the Diaspore mine owner, arrived to pick us up. He asked how we had slept and I remarked that it was my first gem hunting trip since Brazil where I had not had to sleep in a Mosquito net, covered head to toe in spray trying to avoid catching malaria and, therefore I was properly rested. As we drove he pointed out the various feldspar mines and explained the geology of the area. There were three long veins of Bauxite in the area and it was in one of these veins that Diaspore had been found. Unlike other Diaspore, which is often discovered more opaque, this had great clarity and under different lighting conditions appeared to change colour. After an hour or so we left the highway and started to climb a rocky dirt track up the mountain. As we bumped up and down in his four wheel drive, Rod

and I were unusually quiet as we took in the lovely scenery. Eventually I broke the silence and asked Murat how they had found the gemstone in such a remote part of Turkey. I now have a full understanding of how gems are discovered in remote areas of Third World countries, where indigenous tribes people have discovered nature's treasures in and around the areas where they settle. Here in Turkey, we are many miles from the nearest village, and this steep hilly area, with its huge rocky outcrops and forests, is not the sort of place you stumble on a gemstone by accident. Murat explained that the gemstones were discovered by miners as they were extracting

Bauxite. They had discovered the mineral (which is used in the making of the metal aluminum) by following one of the three large veins in the region into the rocky forest. Although there were more accessible areas where the mineral can be mined, this remote location was producing bauxite of a very high commercial grade.

As his 4x4 twisted around a bend, we came across an elderly gentleman descending down the hillside on a mule. He had a brown knitted cardigan wrapped around his head to protect him from the sun, but from his thick leathery skin you could tell he had spent his whole life outdoors. Murat stopped the car and asked the old man what he was doing so far from the village, he informed him that he was a bee keeper and that he had been up in the mountains tending his hives. As the gentleman rode by I questioned Murat about whether he gets nervous seeing locals in the vicinity of his mine. As I travel around gemstone mines all over the world, I see that theft from local communities is one of the biggest issues faced by miners. Even when mines such as the Diaspore mine are fully licensed, with all of the correct authorisations and permits from the government, even when they employ lots of locals creating wealth in the area, even when they pay all of the correct taxes and

take massive gambles on whether their huge investment in equipment and expenses will ever return a profit, some locals believe it's their divine right to try and steal from the mines. I have seen it in Zambia, Mozambique, Brazil and of course in Kenya. Campbell Bridges lost his life over the fact that a group of lawless locals didn't like the fact that a foreigner held a legitimate mining licence. Whilst I am a massive supporter of artisinal mining and supporting indigenous businesses, in mines such as the Diaspore mine, it would be impossible for anyone other than a professional mining company to extract the gemstone. Bauxite is a very tough mineral and the seams where the

gem is discovered is some 40 metres deep inside the hillside. This is the sort of mining that only experienced miners with explosives and expensive equipment can undertake. Put simply, the locals would never be able to benefit from this gemstone without the efforts of a large, well-organised mining operation.

After about half an hour of travelling through the gorgeous sunny landscape, we arrived at the mine. We had just missed a visit from the forestry commission who had popped in for a coffee. Murat explained how one of the biggest dangers in the area was the risk of fire. Throughout the summer

Steve at the entrance to the world's only Csarite mine.

the land becomes very dry and as the forest floor is covered in pine needles (which contain highly flammable tree sap), if a fire does start it can spread alarmingly fast. The managers at the mine work closely with the forestry commission to maintain the road through the hillside which is needed both to act as a boundary to prevent the spread of fire and also as a road for fire engines and the army to use should a fire breakout. Murat is also passionate about the environment and for any tree they remove during the mining process they plant four new ones.

The view from the mine's entrance across the sweeping valley is truly stunning. Right next to the miner lodgings are vividly coloured oleander flowers, over the top of which your eyes feast on the glorious panoramic landscape. The whole experience is further enriched by a loud chorus of sounds from dancing crickets in the top of the trees.

The mine has around 40 employees. Murat explained how he pays all of them a salary higher than the norm for mining in Turkey and that he also provides them all with health insurance. Whilst some of the local miners descend the hillside returning to their homes every night, those miners who have been recruited from

other regions due to their specialised skills, stay in accommodation provided on the mining site.

With Diaspore becoming increasingly hard to discover, Murat had invested heavily in state of the art mining equipment. His sorting tables where all of the rough bauxite is brought to, is as sophisticated as the very best that I have seen. Murat explained that part of his commitments to the government in order for them to keep renewing his mining permit, is to each year extract a certain tonnage of bauxite. Therefore there is a certain need for speed within the mine and as the gemstone is so valuable and incredibly rare, his team of eagle-eyed gem spotters make sure that every single piece of bauxite is examined as it passes them on the conveyor belt, ensuring that not a single Diaspore crystal, no matter how small, is lost in the process.

After we had taken a look at the sorting tables (even though today they are conveyor belts we still tend to refer to them as tables), it was time to put on our safety helmets, light up our torches and enter the mine. The mine has just two entrances and operates on three different levels. To understand the topography of the mine imagine a hotel with three floors. Each corridor being the horizontal mine shafts from which

18

the bauxite is mined, each one being approximately two metres wide and two metres high. The ceiling of the mine is support with logs from the local forest. On the ground floor tunnel they have built a small track on which Indiana Jones-style carts carry the bauxite to the sorting tables. The tunnels on the second and third floor are of similar size and every hundred feet or so a vertical shaft is created to transport the bauxite to the ground level, where it is loaded in to the carts and removed. Effectively they are just like lift shafts. Now, as the bauxite miners are tunnelling along, occasionally they find small seams in the dense rock filled with a mud-like compound. These are the areas where

there is a potential of finding a Diaspore crystal. When this happens, they call in the crystal miners who carefully scrape through the seams with a small hand tool looking for Diaspore.

Murat turned to Rod and I, and asked if we would like to have a go ourselves. "Are you joking?" Rod said and followed it with one of his legendary witty comments. Even under the dimly light torch, I could see his grin was from ear to ear. So after a little tuition and guidance from his chief crystal miner, we were let loose on a small seam. We were like two little kids in a sweet shop. We had a steel bar which was about 12 inches long with

Rod Jinks with his eyes firmly fixed on the prize as he unearths a raw Csarite crystal from the walls of the world's only Csarite mine a hook at the end similar to a needle used for crochet. After a short while I managed to pull out a crystal: it was very small and quite included, but that didn't matter to me, because I had just experienced a feeling that must be like a mountaineer would feel when reaching the peak of an iconic mountain range. It was euphoria at its very best. Then I saw Rod focusing all of his efforts on a tiny little area, he was diligently scraping around the outside of a small object. Eventually the miner lent over and gave him a hand and there it was: in his hand a small true Diaspore crystal, I examined it under torch light, all the time Rod was saying, "Is it good, is it of gem quality, have I unearthed one,

is it facetable grade?" After I gave it a little wipe, I held it to the torch and viewing it through both axes I could see it was indeed a fine crystal that might yield a gem of approximately three quarters of a carat. Here we were in the only Diaspore mine on the planet ,and following closely behind the work of the bauxite miners we were able to extract two small raw crystals. Whilst mine was heavily included and not of a facetable grade, Rod's piece was breathtaking.

When I asked Murat how often they uncovered crystals in these muddy seams, he explained that sometimes you can find no gems for a very long

Steve Bennett looking for this most elusive of gemstones

time and then you can hit an area where it is fairly lucrative. He explained that for every 100 grams they found, only 1 or 2 per cent would be of a gem quality.

Unlike other underground mines that I have visited, like the Amethyst mines in Rio Grande where you are searching for geodes, or the underground Emerald mines of Itabira and Zambia where you are trying to find the edge of a pegmatite, (an area known as the reaction zone), Diaspore is found in small seams within dense bauxite which are not more than one or two inches in width.

After we had finished working the area Murat suggested we let the professional crystal miners back to the rock face and we would travel up to the second shaft where they were widening a tunnel and excavating bauxite. As we travelled along the second layer Murat explained that in this shaft, they currently were not finding many seams and when they did come across one it rarely yielded any crystals. As we arrived at the area where the miners were working, they had just finished drilling holes in to the rock face and their explosives expert was busy pushing dynamite into each one. As the host rock in this mine is so dense, it's quicker to progress with explosives than it is with compressor-hammers and chisels. First the miners

Dynamite is used to blast away the rocks in the search for the gem.

drill holes into the rock which are around two feet deep and just the right width for the stick of dynamite to be inserted. After the last stick was in position, we watched as he plugged the holes, wired all of the connections together and then we all retreated some 20 to 30 metres back along the tunnel. I was too excited and too busy watching as the wire was connected to the detonator and its arm cranked round and round to deliver the charge, that I failed to notice that Rod and all of the miners had covered their ears with their hands. Bang! A deafening sound hit us like the boom of a plane breaking the sound barrier; the ceiling of the mine shaft shook and you could hear the sound of falling rocks

and rubble in the distance. Then came the plume of dust: it was all incredibly exhilarating, and as soon as it was safe to do so we returned to the rock face to see how much progress had been made.

The four sticks of dynamite had only managed to break a segment of approximately four foot high and two foot wide from the side of the shaft. I was amazed at how much work and effort goes into this mine. It's almost as if Mother Nature decided that as the gem was so stunningly beautiful, with gorgeous pleochroism, with a wonderful subtle colour change, a change that seems to vary in every different type of light, a gem that exudes brilliance

A huge piece of rough Diaspore. Csarite, the colour change variety, is extremely rare and seldom found.

and dispersion, that with all of these wonderful features she was going to make it as difficult to extract as possible. Firstly, she placed it high up in the mountains making it difficult even to get to the mine, then you have to tunnel through 40 metres of limestone even just to arrive at the start of the bauxite, then the rock is so incredibly difficult to extract, that you literally have to blast your way through it. Even when you arrive at the right zone, it's only every now and then, almost randomly, that you come across a seam that has one or two crystals embedded in it. But just to make sure the gem remains one of the rarest on the planet, Mother Nature then decided that only one or two in every hundred would be of a gem quality!

As we came out of the dark yet cool tunnel, we were greeted by an outside temperature of some 38 degrees, I commented to Rod that it's how an ice cube must feel as it's taken out of a cool dark fridge and dropped into a warm glass. We were then treated to a huge Turkish salad that the mine's chef had prepared, and we sat eating it overlooking the wonderful scenery.

Both Rod and I had had a fabulous time. We both commented how we would love to have spent the whole day inside the mine trying to unearth more pieces, but Murat explained that whilst they are working on a good seam, it's best not to delay the professionals. He asked me what my view was and if I had any questions. "Only the one", I said, How soon can you get me another good shipment? We both laughed at my rhetorical question and Murat just told me to be patient and he would try and get me another delivery as soon as he could.

So how do I summarise my Diaspore experience? The mine is located in a beautiful landscape, it is mined by a passionate team of people and at the head of the company is a gentleman who is dedicated to the gemstone, the community and the environment. I was pleased to learn that Murat - as well as working hard with the forestry commission - also financially supports the local school. It was great to meet a miner that had almost identical views to my company. Both of us work on and support environmental projects and we both support schools (the only difference is that Murat's school is a local school and mine is some 3000 miles from where I live).

I learnt that his mine is fairly difficult to get to, there is no electricity, no running water and therefore every aspect of the mining operation is a challenge. The Diaspore team are very competent, well organised and very professional. The gem is incredibly difficult to locate and so far has only ever been discovered in this one mine. Whilst there are several other gemstones that are only found in one region (Tanzanite in Arusha, and Mookite in the Mooka Creek in Australia) or in some instances on just one hillside (Larimar in the Dominican Republic), Diaspore is the only precious gemstone that is only found in just one mine. That makes it incredibly rare. Today Murat's mine still extracts and sells the mineral bauxite and it's a good job that he does too, as Diaspore is not found on a consistent basis.

Diaspore is certainly one of the ultimate, rare, natural treasures of nature.

Special Feature
Presenters' visit to the Csarite mine,
as told by Adina Stubbs

One night in Turkey... a lifetime of love for Csarite.

When Steve asked Ruth Linnett and me to travel to Turkey, my eyes lit up with excitement. Here was a chance to see for myself what all the fuss was about with this amazing new gem that has caused such a dispute over the last few years. To be there and speak to Murat, the mine owner, and see for myself the very surroundings where this gem was born was too good an opportunity to pass up. Even though we were only there for a day and a night, the answer was most definitely yes! Matt, our resident gemologist and camera man, was part of team too and we were all very excited. So the journey begins on a Monday lunchtime when we were taken to the airport. With great difficulty packing light, I eagerly awaited being picked up. Sadly I had to leave the wedges behind, and the only other sensible footwear I had was flip flops so they would have to do. Thankfully, when we got to the mine, Murat had some sensible footwear for me to borrow! But we'll get to that later.

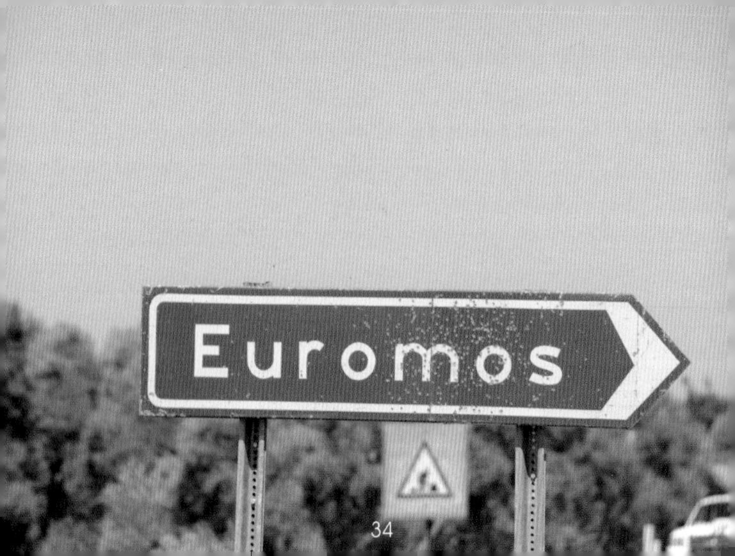
Euromos

After long delays at the airport (and some serious shopping as a consequence) we arrived in Turkey late that night to meet the mine owner, Murat, and his friend, Ali, who would later be our guide and friend too. Murat was tall (about the same height as Ruth), softly spoken and very modest. When we got to the hotel Murat told us the story of the dispute over the name and the rights to the gem over the years. Complicated as it may seem to be, it was simple to me. Everyone seemed to be fighting over this gem but one thing was clear, we were talking to the mine owner direct and the relationship was one of mutual respect and passion. We were there at the mine and Murat was going to show us around the next day, before we got on the plane back home in the evening. That's all that counted. It was going to be brief but intense, and definitely long lasting. So to bed we went, and not that early may I add, as we were buzzing from the prospect of what we would discover tomorrow. After all, I'd never been mining before!

Early next morning after a lavish breakfast Murat met us for the trip. We were going to stop off just before we reached the mine at the beautiful Euromos, an ancient city built in the 2nd Century C.E. and remarkably, still standing there, was the Temple of Zeus looking majestic, tall, nestled in olive groves and no doubt with many stories to tell. It is one of the few remaining and most important ancient cities in all of Asia.

Excavations only began in 1969 and as I stood there wide-eyed and incensed by the powerful scent of pine and the orchestra of crickets, I wondered, what if the ancient people of Euromos bejewelled themselves with the beautiful Csarite we were about to see?

The temple of Zeus at Euromos.

A faceted Csarite gleaming in its homeland.

A newly mined Csarite crystal.

Mine owner Murat with a fine example of precious Csarite.

*The naturally photogenic Csarite in a beautiful ring,
against the backdrop of the Anatolian mountain.*

We had a beautiful large Csarite ring that we wanted to photograph by the ancient city of Euromos, as it was so close to the mine. Matt placed it on the rock and began to take pictures. We watched in the glaring heat and as the sun beat down on this gemstone it became clear to me that this gem was a natural! No "this is my best side" or posing. Amazingly, like some sort of out-of-this-world shape shifter or changeling, it absorbed the beauty of its surroundings and radiated them back tenfold! The sunlight, the pale olive greens of the olive trees and gold of the earth and ancient rock around it gleamed from within. "Wow", I thought silently. Then I became excited at the feeling we must be very close to our destination.

After some more filming work with Matt we got back in our 4x4s. It was at this point that Steve let me wear this magical Csarite ring for the rest of the breathtaking climb into the Anatolian mountains, and indeed for the rest of the day until the sunset on our journey back to the airport!

I had read the description of the short drive up the mountain from Rod and Steve's trip last year but nothing could have prepared me for the real experience. The pungent intoxicating smell of pine trees, the clear blue sky, the gleaming sunlight the pinky peach (or was it peachy pink...) flowers, the golden copper dry ground. Then there was the sound of crickets and the green all around and the biggest jaw dropper was when we got to the top and saw the views for miles over the Anatolian mountains. This was the only place in the world, this very spot, where we would find this gemstone, this mystery, called Csarite

Cameraman & gemologist Matt Bennett, shooting the amazing scenery.

The glorious Anatolian mountains.

We were greeted by the very friendly adopted resident dog and the overwhelming sound of crickets. They occasional softened their music for our filming but this was hit and miss and if it wasn't the crickets the wind would get in the way. It seemed Mother Nature was making it very difficult to somehow capture or talk about the beauty of this gem. Was she protecting it perhaps? Our first stop was a small padlocked office which held a year's supply of this gemstone (not much at all). There were also some incredible minerals they'd found along the way including many examples of twinning, something I'd only read about during my gem studies over the years, and rutile needles suspended like threads mid gem. I loved seeing in real life what I had read about.

The miners were having their lunch and were all perfectly dressed in uniform - orange boiler suits with hard hats.

After some more filming with Murat we were brought down for an amazing lunch by the chef there. He was once a 5 star hotel chef and now makes the food for all the miners. It was divine I can tell you. I even recognised a childhood dish my mum used to make me. She's Romanian and I guess the food culture must cross over.

After lunch it was time to get down to the hard work - the mining. We got changed into our borrowed attire, including some big black shoes-after all, there was no way I could wear flip flops! After quite a bit of giggling from us and with amused looks from the miners we went down to the mine entrance. First we had a go at sorting through the bauxite. Bauxite is the main mining operation and there is a certain tonnage that needs to be produced throughout the year to carry on the operation. So, as we sorted through the big, medium and small pieces, washing and checking them for signs of treasure along the conveyer belt, it became clear that we were extremely slow and would probably be best leave it to the professionals.

57

Next, we walked up to the mine entrance and watched the Indiana Jones-style carts full of bauxite being tipped into the conveyer belt by two men at a time. Again, this was back breaking work but I wanted to prove a point and tip the cart and be part of it! Murat explained that maybe 1 in 20 carts could contain a piece of Csarite. I was feeling quite hot by this point and thinking this is going to be a long day.

Steve Bennett &
Murat Akgun at the
mine's entrance.

60

Still we had not entered the mine so we begin our journey on foot, in the dark, with our torched hard hats in place. As we went deeper into the mine, with the muddy tracks and narrow climbs on makeshift ladders, it became very clear to me why flip flops and wedges just wouldn't do. The air was pleasantly cool but as we progressed deeper it also became thin, and at one point I thought I was going to pass out.

After sitting down for a few minutes and having a drink I soon adjusted, and was more than able to continue. In fact I was now determined to find that winning piece of Csarite. The tunnels narrowed to about 1 to 2 metres high and wide, and with a bucket and pick we stopped every now and again to see the possible finds. We could clearly see a vein and the rock seemed to crumble away, but unfortunately as we picked away the potential Csarite crumbled too. Several times we got excited thinking we'd found the piece, but it definitely wasn't gem quality. I'm not one to give up, and considered at one point going off in an unknown part of the mine or a blocked off tunnel but reasoned it probably wouldn't go down too well if a TGGC presenter got lost in a mine in Turkey! So beguiling is this gem, and so determined I was to find her... the one... she nearly lured me in another direction altogether. So after hours of searching we found - well - nothing... at least nothing that could be gem quality.

ACİL
ÇIKIŞ

After a hard days mining, Adina, Matt and Ruth.

We came out of the mine into the sunshine as adventurers. It would have looked cool except we were dressed from head to toe in oversized orange boiler suits with big hard hats on. Not exactly the Lara Croft image I had in my head! Anyway, I felt pleased with my efforts and it made me realise how extraordinarily difficult it was to come upon this unique treasure.

Planting new trees, as agreed with the Turkish forestry commission.

The day was drawing to a close and we still had one more thing to do - help plant some trees. Murat explained that whilst the majority of the mining is underground and causes minimal damage to the environment around it, there is a programme in place with the Forestry Commission ensuring there are always new trees planted on a regular basis so there is minimal carbon footprint and in fact more then anything does a huge bit for the environment. We ascended the hill and planted the trees. The descent however was less graceful and we more or less slid, or maybe more accurately rolled down the hill like bowling balls in fits of giggles!

Murat takes his responsibilities for the environment seriously and plants new trees on a regular basis.

75

The end of our day was approaching and we said goodbye to the friendly amazing team that had been so hospitable throughout the day. It was finished off by the most beautiful sunset over the Anatolian mountains and as we drove to the airport I looked at the beautiful ring Steve had lent me for the day and I couldn't help thinking that the colours in the sky perfectly matched the colours in this magical mystical gem we know as Csarite. The sunset, clichéd as it might sound, sealed the memory of my trip to the Csarite mine forever. Although I tried to persuade Steve to let us stay another day, till the minute we got on the plane, I know I would be eternally grateful for this wonderful experience.

You see, if you look at factors that make this gemstone so desirable: pleochroism, fire, colour change and extreme rarity, plus the fact you can only get it from one mine in the world, you understand why there has been such a fight over this incredible gemstone.

The finished product
at the end of its
unpredictable and
priceless journey.

It became clear to me, whether it was because I was so high up in the heady heights of the Anatolian mountains, or had been taken by its ability to absorb its surroundings of gold, apricot, peach, olive, copper pink and reflect only beauty, or even whether it was because I was frustrated by my inability to find even a single piece of gem quality at the mine with hours of searching, I was definitely in love Csarite.

A night in Turkey gave me a day in the Csarite mine, which was enough to appreciate how lucky we are to have this natural and miraculous gem in our hands.

The incredible hard-working miners at the entrance to their Diaspore mine.

Adina holding a
mined Csarite crystal..

One shopping
destination

THE GENUINE
GEMSTONE
COMPANY

Special Feature
Customer's Mining Visit Diary

I was incredibly lucky just recently to be invited to visit the Csarite mine organised by Steve Bennett. It's a day I will never forget and was a superb experience not just for me but my family too! So, without further ado, this is what happened...

We had arranged to meet the mine's General Manager, Ali, at the mining company's office in the nearest town to the mine, Milas. It was a four hour drive from our villa and the heat was so intense (in the high 40s) we were dressed for the beach! On the phone the night before, Ali had assured us that we would be provided with all the protective equipment/clothing we needed, so we turned up in our flip flops and sunglasses. At the office we had to sign an insurance waiver in case anything happened – which did make me stop and think whether we should take our 9 year old, Katya, but she was so excited there was no turning back! . Then we had to sign a confidentiality/secrecy agreement stating we wouldn't divulge the location of the mine etc. We signed on the dotted line and then bundled ourselves into Ali's pickup for the hour long drive to the Mine.

After a short journey we turned off the main road onto a bumpy unmade road and for about 45 minutes had a bone shaking ride up winding mountain roads through dense pine groves, glimpsing wild horses and Lycian ruins dotted around and between clearings. It's a good job that Katya's loose tooth had fallen out the night before otherwise that journey would certainly have made the tooth fairy fly out to Turkey.

Finally we reached the top of the mountain and entered a small open clearing lined with various buildings, some that housed the 30 mine workers (who live there) and others containing mining equipment and various other unidentifiable bits and pieces. The air in the mountain was lovely and clear but it was still very, very hot. The view was breathtaking and I hadn't appreciated how high we had driven. I certainly wouldn't want to be the person sent for provisions only to realise I'd forgotton the milk!

So, after a quick slurp of water we got back into the pickup and drove another few minutes to the entrance of the mine. I have to say that this was one of those times where I had an "oh my goodness" moment, as we had to take a sharp right hand bend to the entrance with a sheer drop on our left hand side. The pickup was too big to go around the bend so we had to go forward and then reverse back a bit (so the drop was RIGHT behind us) and inch our way around. If you've ever seen the film 'The Italian Job' you may recall the last scene with the coach? Well, I could see us all leaning forward willing the pickup not to roll back as Ali changed gear and moved forward slowly. You can see the road and the lack of width of it (and get an idea of the drop) in the photo on page 86.

We had arrived! We were at the mine entrance and Orhan the chief miner came out to meet us. After a few introductions we established that he didn't speak English but thankfully my husband is Turkish so we had our own translator. Orhan gave us all hard hats with a light that we could attach (or hold) with a lead to a battery pack that we tucked into an appropriate waistband. We suddenly realised that this was the only equipment we were going to be given, so we are officially the only mine-visiting, flip-flop

wearing visitors they've probably had! .Anyway, that wasn't going to deter us and we went into the mine, dressed for the beach but in a hard hat.

I should point out that it was at this moment as we were walking towards the mine entrance that it occurred to me that I'm seriously claustrophobic. Yep, I'd been so excited that I'd glossed over that part in my mind and in truth I hadn't realised we were going to go into the mine and I thought we might just see where they sort the rough or something like that. Okay, not one of my better thought processes but never mind, I was committed and was going into that mine claustrophobia or not!

We walked into the mine entrance and the first thing that hit us was the drastic drop in temperature. We had literally gone from over 40 degrees outside the entrance to probably about 10 degrees inside. The cold dropped just a few metres inside – not even deep inside the mine. Another thing that was a surprise was how high the mine was (about 2 metres) so it didn't feel too cramped and it was also about 2 metres wide so we could walk side by side. The reason for that became apparent later on.

The walls and ceiling are shored up by timber struts spread about a metre apart and you can see the walls of the mine clearly through them. Orhan explained that the bauxite deposit (an aluminium ore) was first discovered in 1949 but it wasn't until 1962 that mining first began. Initially, the government issued licences only for bauxite, so any Diaspore couldn't be mined until 2005 when new mining laws led to a private mining company re-opening the mine for Csarite. The new laws permitted them to secure a mining permit and so today the mine produces mainly bauxite but also has a smaller find of Csarite. It's not mined in huge quantities and because it has perfect cleavage, Csarite is incredibly challenging to facet so some rough can't be faceted at all. To give you an indication of how small the supply is, while Diaspore was first discovered in 1801 in the Ural Mountains in Russia, the Turkish deposit remains the world's only source of Turkish Diaspore (Csarite). So, unlike Diamonds, it really isn't found in huge quantities. Couple that with the difficulty of cutting it and you start to begin to understand the rarity of good size/well cut specimens. I've certainly got a new found appreciation for it.

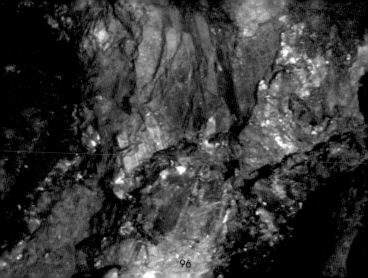

As we moved deeper into the mine, the light from the entrance tunnel disappeared (another "oh my goodness" moment for me) but suddenly you could see the floor glittering as if tiny stars had fallen all over the muddy floor. Orhan explained that this was the aluminium and the black was caused by the iron. Orhan has worked in mining for over 20 years, including 5 years at the Csarite mine, and he clearly loves his job. He would just stop every now and again by a bit of wall and would point out a crystal Csarite or mica (a silicate mineral that looks like Mother of Pearl) and say things like "that's not a good one"! I've collected gemstones for years and can tell a well cut gemstone from a bad one. However, rough is something I've not had the opportunity to study much so I was incredibly impressed at his ability to look at a piece of seemingly innocuous wall and determine what was good and what wasn't! Apparently, this (pictured) isn't a good bit of crystal.

The mine itself is 400 metres long but it then stretches up 100 metres and down 100 metres. To move between levels there are cut outs to the side walls with precarious wood ladders that are used to go up and down. The miners literally scamper up and down them like mountain goats but we were less successful and in the darkness it was really odd not being able to see where you were putting your feet, so there was much banging of hard hats against walls and scraping of hands against unseen parts of the mine!

Photo on far left taken with flash. This page is the same angle with only the light from the helmet.

A seam in the mine wall that may indicate the presence of Csarite

To get the material out of the mine, a digger type thing (you can tell I'm not into those), thunders into the mine and scoops up material to take out. It dawned on me that the reason the mine is the height and width it is, is because of this machine, you could only just squeeze to each side of it when it was in the mine. Clearly the digger can't get to all floors as getting up the ladders would be problematic so at certain points there are open sections of floor leading from an upper to a lower floor lined with a metal shute that material is put into and collected into containers below that glide on railway lines.

At different points along the way we would meet a miner working away and digging out the seams or standing on a platform surveying a seam in the ceiling. They were so relaxed and seemed really enthusiastic about what they were doing.

At one point, Orhan stopped, bent down and literally picked up a Csarite crystal off the floor! I was amazed. I can normally spot a gemstone at a hundred paces but in the darkness I couldn't find anything! This crystal is apple green in daylight but at night time in incandescent lighting it turns a peach/brown colour. If it were to be cut, I would expect that it would only produce a gem of around 0.5ct. You can see the size of it in the photo opposite, most of it would be lost in the cutting process. Apologies for the poor quality photos of the crystal but they were taken inside the mine with only the light from the helmet.

In a few locations were small containers of mined crystals waiting for transportation out of the mine. Some were quite large but they all seemed to be an elongated shape caused by the mineral structure as you can see from the photos.

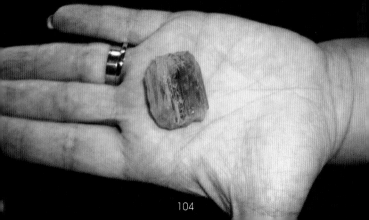

Left: Container of newly mined crystals.
Above: An example of a large crystal.

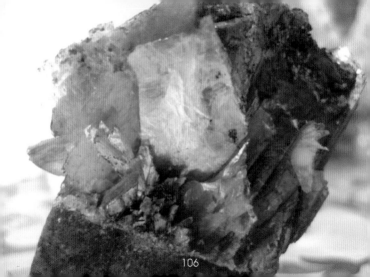

Orhan stopped again and literally with his bare hands pulled a chunk of the wall away that had crystal and mica all through it and handed it to me! Claustraphobia? Not any more! I was beyond myself with excitement seeing the wonders that nature had created. Here is a photo (left) that I took of it outside in daylight and you can see the Mother of Pearl effect created by the mica.

I have to say that there were some odd things that I didn't expect. For example, would you believe that there are midges flying around, attracted by the lights? If you stand still they literally cover you in minutes which isn't the most pleasant thing on earth and if I ever become a miner, I'll be the fastest miner ever to avoid being swarmed! Also, the damp and darkness meant that huge bizarre looking mushrooms were growing along the floors. I meant to take a photo of them but forgot; but they looked like huge, white, spidery alien mushrooms. Very strange indeed. The only thing I really didn't like was hearing the huge digger on a floor above and the stones dropping from the roof as it moved around, together with hearing the vibration of the machine working. That was unnerving.

Believe it or not, we were in the mine for over an hour and it was fascinating, strange, weird, unexpected and a hundred other emotions that I can't even begin to mention. Most importantly, it was FANTASTIC. I would do it again in a heartbeat.

When we emerged back into the heat and light of the day, we were taken back to the main station and had a cup of Turkish coffee. Orhan told us about the seams and how the earth makes the gems and he clearly was incredibly knowledgeable – he wasn't just a miner – he was a gemmologist as well. It's also important to say that the living/pay conditions etc. for the mine workers are excellent and I believe that has a lot to do with the affiliation with The Genuine Gemstone Company. There's a huge emphasis on ethical mining and you get a real sense of that when you're there. Having lived in Turkey, I know that workers in some industries are not given health insurance or basic conditions that you and I would think of as normal but that's not the case for the mine workers. They are looked after really well.

So at 4pm we headed back down the mountain and back to reality... sort of! As we were winding our way down the mountain a wild stallion decided to challenge the pick up to a duel and literally launched itself at the front of the pickup! Ali slammed on the brakes, we lurched forward in our seats but thankfully he avoided the stallion that galloped off, unhurt, into the forest!